"My weight is always perfect for my height — which varies."

"My weight is always perfect for my height — which varies."

More Sylvia by Nicole Hollander

St. Martin's Press , New York

Library of Congress Cataloging in Publication Data

Hollander, Nicole.
   My weight is always perfect for my height—which
varies.

   I. Title.
PN6728.S97H6   1982   741.5'973   82-10587

ISBN: 0-312-55861-9

Design by Tom Greensfelder
Jacket photo by Steve Kagan

First Edition
10 9 8 7 6 5 4 3 2 1

5

6

8

CAN YOU DRAW THIS CAT?

13

BE SURE AND STAY TUNED FOR "PULL MY LEG"

THE SHOW WHERE VETERAN POLITICAL REPORTERS ASK OUR GOVERNMENT OFFICIALS HARD QUESTIONS,

AND THEN LAUGH OUT LOUD AT THEIR ANSWERS.

"ADOPT-A-DOG" TURNED DOWN BETTY AND JOE...

BUMMER!

NO ONE'S AT HOME DURING THE DAY, AND THE PUPPY MIGHT GET LONELY...

I CAN SEE THAT.

...AND THEIR APARTMENT IS TOO SMALL FOR THE PUP TO HAVE HIS OWN ROOM.

YOU NEVER KNOW WHEN TO STOP.

Sylvia On Sunday

18

REMEMBER YOUR KITCHEN is A STORE HOUSE of INEXPENSIVE BEAUTY PRODUCTS: OATMEAL FOR A FACIAL SCRUB, AND

SIR, WHAT IS THE MOST IRRITATING THING PEOPLE DO IN PUBLIC?

SINGING OPERA IN ELEVATORS.

NO, WAIT.... TAP DANCING IN ELEVATORS.

SO PROBABLY THE MOST IRRITATING THING SOMEONE COULD DO IS TAP DANCE TO OPERA IN AN ELEVATOR?

HUH?

MEMO TO CHANEL, LANVIN, MATCHABELLI, HALSTON. RE: 2 PERFUME NAMES FOR THE 80'S.

PURGATORY: THE PERFUME THAT'S ALMOST SINFUL.

OPTIONS EXCHANGE: THE PERFUME THAT MAKES MEN RISK EVERYTHING.

MA, HOW LONG YOU GONNA BE IN THERE?

RITA, HONEY, I'M REDECORATING. COULD YOU USE THE BATHROOM AT HARRY'S BAR?

"Hot"   PRIME

MA, I HATE DRYING OFF WITH PAPER TOWELS.

THE NUTROANALYST IS IN

RATES
FOWL   5.00
BEEF   7.00
SEAFOOD SEASON-AL

I ANALYZE CHARACTER THROUGH FOOD PREFERENCE.

HEY, I'M GAME. GO AHEAD.

PICK YOUR FAVORITE.
① CHICKEN CORDON BLEU.
② SLICED CHICKEN SANDWICH.
③ CHICKEN VESUVIO.

SLICED CHICKEN SANDWICH.

BABYISH, EASILY MANIPULATED, NO GREAT SHAKES AS A LOVER, PROBABLY BORN IN A WESTERN STATE, NOT CALIFORNIA.

AMAZING.

27

MA, HOW LONG ARE YOU GOING TO BE IN THERE?

RITA, HAIR GROWS AT THE RATE OF $\frac{1}{2}$" A MONTH...

CHECK BACK IN NOVEMBER.

37

38

40

41

Sylvia on Sunday

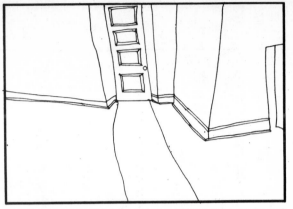

They said the house was dangerous for a young girl at night.

THAT ROOM WAS LOCKED...HAD BEEN FOR AS LONG AS SHE COULD REMEMBER. AT NIGHT WHEN THE HOUSE WAS STILL, SHE COULD HEAR SOMEONE MOVING AROUND IN THERE.

THUMP, THUMP.

THEY WARNED HER ABOUT WANDERING AROUND THE HOUSE AT NIGHT...

BUT AGAIN AND AGAIN SHE WAS DRAWN TO THAT DOOR.

NOW SHE TOUCHED IT AND IT SWUNG OPEN. A VOICE WHISPERED HER NAME... "FELICITY."

IT WAS WILLIAM POWELL, A SCOTCH ON THE ROCKS IN ONE HAND AND A PEACH SATIN PEIGNOIR, TRIMMED WITH MARABOU, IN THE OTHER...

OH YEAH.

43

47

M.D. FantAsies

PEOPLE WILL BOW TO YOU
IN THE STREETS, SING
YOUR PRAISES, SHOWER
YOU WITH COINS, AND
THEN SUE YOU FOR
MALPRACTICE.

DR. ROGER "FATS" DAVIS IS WITH US TODAY TO TALK ABOUT HIS REVOLUTIONARY DIET PLAN

ROGER, IS YOUR DIET DIFFICULT TO STAY ON?

NOT REALLY, PATTY, BUT IT DOES INVOLVE A CERTAIN COMMITMENT.

FOR INSTANCE: YOU HAVE TO BE WILLING TO SLEEP 12-16 HOURS A DAY.

I COULD GET BEHIND THAT.

DON'T ASK THE BARTENDER TO MIX SILLY DRINKS

49

A RECENT POLL SHOWS THAT FOR MOST OLDER AMERICANS PROBLEMS OF POVERTY, LONELINESS, AND FEAR OF CRIME ARE A <u>MYTH</u>.

THERE ARE HOWEVER FOUR GROUPS THAT REPORT A DISMAL EXISTENCE.

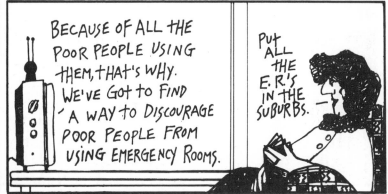

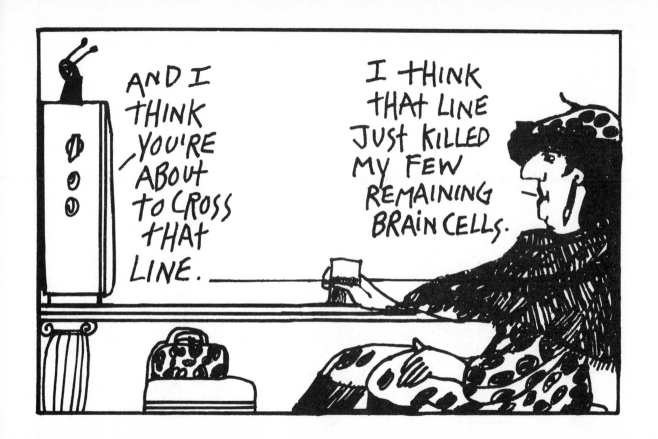

VETERINARIANS LIKE CATS AS PATIENTS BECAUSE THEY HEAL QUICKLY,

AND BECAUSE CAT OWNERS PAY THEIR BILLS FASTER THAN DOG OWNERS.

THE CHECK IS IN THE MAIL.

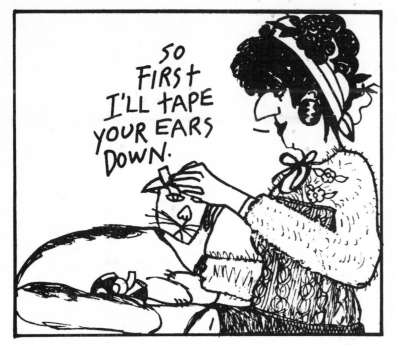

65

72

An aRtist goes to A foRtuNe teLLeR

73

Sylvia on Sunday

THIS IS PATTY MURPHY. I'M ON VACATION THIS WEEK, BUT DON'T TOUCH THAT DIAL! STAY TUNED FOR THE "RIGHTEOUS WOMAN'S HOUR" WITH YOUR HOSTESS BETTY SMITH, WHO WILL MAKE YOU LONG FOR MY RETURN.

YET I WASN'T HAPPY. WHENEVER I EXPRESSED DOUBTS, BOB TOOK ME ON ANOTHER VACATION.

BOB, WE ARE ON THE EDGE OF THE VOID.

I'LL GET THE TRAVELERS' CHECKS.

74

75

76

TODAY THE CITY ANNOUNCED IT WOULD WITHDRAW ALL SERVICES...

NEWSBREAK WITH PATTY MURPHY

AT MIDNIGHT UNLESS...

$65,000,000 IS LEFT IN A BROWN PAPER BAG AT THE BIG FOUNTAIN IN THE PARK.

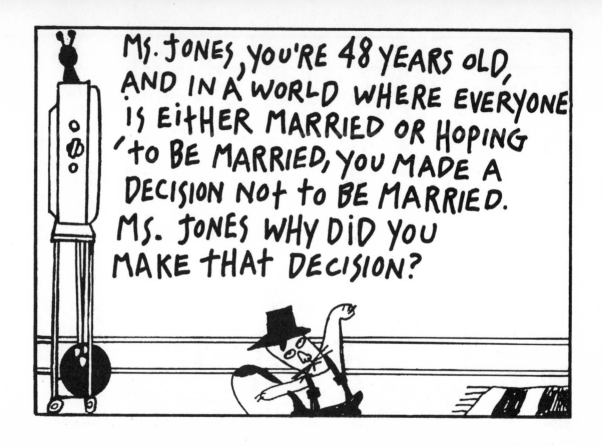

83

I'M TIRED OF MEN WHO NEVER HEAR A WORD I SAY.

I SEE A VERY NEAT MAN WHO IS INTERESTED IN EVERYTHING YOU DO...

SOUNDS GRAND

WHO YOU SEE, WHERE YOU GO, YOUR MAIL.

WHAT IS HE, SOME KIND OF JEALOUS NUT?

F.B.I., ASSIGNED TO YOUR YOGA GROUP.

HARRY, HOW DID YOU LIKE THE WEDDING I DID FOR TINA AND GEORGE?

IT WAS A GREAT WEDDING.

WEDDINGS BY SYLVIA

WHAT DID YOU LIKE BEST ABOUT IT? THE SPACE ODYSSEY MOTIF?

I LIKED THAT WE GOT TO EAT DURING THE CEREMONY.

THOSE WERE TERRIFIC HOT DOGS.

BETTER THAN THE BALL PARK.

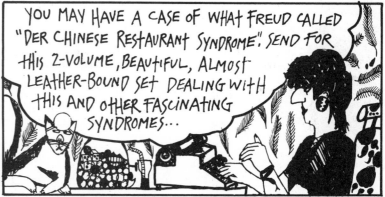

A woman goes to a fortune teller

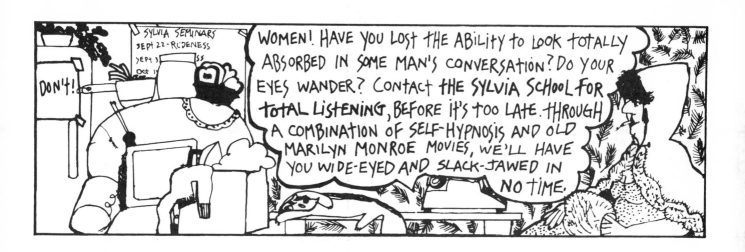

92

97

100

101

MA, WOULD YOU BE UPSET IF WE HAD A DIFFERENT KIND OF THANKSGIVING MEAL THIS YEAR?

HONEY, WHATEVER YOU WANT IS FINE WITH ME.

TURKEY, STUFFING, SWEET POTATOES, CRANBERRY SAUCE.

HOW ABOUT THE SHRIMP IN BLACK BEAN AND GARLIC SAUCE INSTEAD OF THE PRESSED ALMOND DUCK?

SO HERE IT IS HARRY, THE BIG NIGHT. THE NIGHT BAR OWNERS LOOK FORWARD TO. IN A FEW HOURS COUNTLESS REVELERS WILL COME THROUGH THOSE DOORS...

LOOKING FOR THAT LAST BIG BLAST OF '81. THEY'LL BE DRINKING, SINGING, LAUGHING, FIGHTING AND GETTING SICK. DO YOU HAVE ANY SPECIAL PLANS FOR CROWD CONTROL?

I'M CLOSING IN 5 MINUTES.

103

THE SYLVIA FILM SCRIPT-WRITING KIT. PART II: THE FEMALE FRIENDSHIP FILM.

CHARACTERS: 2 ATTRACTIVE OLDER WOMEN. LOCALE: EXPENSIVE INTERIORS, RURAL/URBAN/BEACH. CLOTHES: NICE. RELATIONSHIP: HAVE NOTHING IN COMMON AND DON'T LIKE EACH OTHER, BUT ARE FRIENDS/OR

THEY LIKE EACH OTHER FOR REASONS THAT ARE OBSCURE TO WOMEN IN THE AUDIENCE. OBLIGATORY FIGHT SCENE: LOTS OF MIS-DIRECTED HITTING AND CRYING.

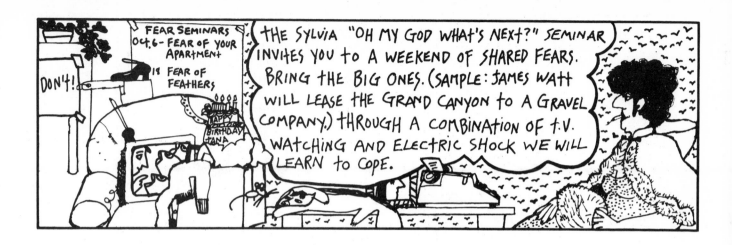

Sylvia on Sunday

PERHAPS I'M BEING PRESUMPTUOUS—

HUSBAND, THOUGHTLESSLY HAVING A FEW HARMLESS DRINKS WITH ASSOCIATE AT HOTEL BAR, FORGETS TO PHONE HOME.

WRIST WATCH IGNORED

TELEPHONE AT BAR

DEAR MA BELL, YOUR "REACH OUT AND TOUCH SOMEONE" COMMERCIALS ARE TERRIFIC, BUT I THINK I HAVE 2 SURE FIRE WAYS TO GET MORE FOLKS TO REACH FOR THE PHONE:

FEAR AND GUILT. HERE'S THE SCENARIO: MAN ON BUSINESS TRIP. WIFE AT HOME, WAITING TO HEAR FROM HIM.

Nicole Hollander

CUT TO WIFE WAITING AT HOME FOR HUSBAND'S CALL. SHE LOOKS LOVINGLY AT HIS PICTURE.

CLOCK

PHOTOS OF KIDS

TELEPHONE

TIME PASSES. SHE GROWS UNDERSTANDABLY RESTIVE. STILL NO CALL.

WIFE TURNS HUSBAND'S PHOTO FACE DOWN AND HEADS FOR THE "CHEATING PART OF TOWN."

THE SYLVIA GUIDES ETIQUETTE

So You'RE GOING tO BE MARRIED.

ELOPEMENTS: THERE ARE MANY REASONS FOR SECRET MARRIAGES. PERHAPS YOU CAN'T AFFORD A BIG WEDDING, OR YOUR FAMILY OBJECTS TO YOUR CHOICE, OR YOUR FIANCÉ IS WANTED BY THE LAW—WHATEVER THE REASON, THINK it OVER CAREFULLY BEFORE DEPRIVING EVERYONE OF A CHANCE to SHARE YOUR HAPPINESS AND A GOOD PARTY.

THERE'S NO PLACE FOR SPECIAL TREATMENT IN THE BUSINESS WORLD.

IF WOMEN WANT TIME OFF to BEAR CHILDREN, THEY CAN'T EXPECT to BE TREATED AS EQUALS.

THE SYLVIA WORD OF THE MONTH FOR ASPIRING MAGAZINE WRITERS IS: TRYST

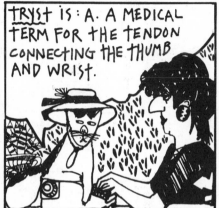

TRYST IS: A. A MEDICAL TERM FOR THE TENDON CONNECTING THE THUMB AND WRIST.

B. A CRACKER, LIKE SHREDDED WHEAT, ONLY SMALLER.

C. SOMETHING PEOPLE DO ON SOAP OPERAS.

Cat
cutouts

Liver

FACIAL HAIR

BEAUTY spot

113

116

117

THE BANKING INDUSTRY ANNOUNCED TODAY THAT CUSTOMERS WHO CONSISTENTLY FALL BELOW THE MINIMUM BALANCE IN THEIR CHECKING ACCOUNTS...

WILL NOT BE ALLOWED TO USE BANKS ANYMORE.

NEWS & PATTY

"THEY CAN KEEP THEIR MONEY UNDER THE MATTRESS FOR ALL WE CARE," SAID AN INDUSTRY SPOKESMAN.

INTERVIEW #4, JAMES WATT: "SYL, YOU'VE SEEN ONE CANYON YOU'VE SEEN 'EM ALL. BELIEVE ME IT'S BORING. BUT AN OFF-SHORE OIL RIG AT NIGHT,

THAT'S POETRY," HE SAID, FLASHING ME THAT SHY CHERUBIC SMILE WE KNOW SO WELL.

119

LUCKILY, I'M NOT ONE OF THOSE WOMEN WHO HAVE TO — WORK.

ROSE, HOWARD COULD GET HIT BY A GOLF CART...

HOWARD HAS PROVIDED FOR US. —

DRIVEN BY A CURLY-HEADED BLONDE WHO SHOOTS IN THE HIGH 70's

PERHAPS A PART-TIME JOB AT A BOUTIQUE.

ANIMAL MASKS

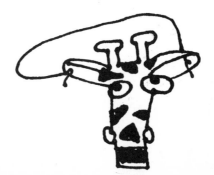

121

HARRY, I GOT A LETTER FROM MY BOOK CLUB.

"DEAR MEMBER, OBVIOUSLY YOU don't CARE A WHIT ABOUT PAYING YOUR BILL; YOUR KIND NEVER DOES. IF YOU don't MAKE PAYMENT ON YOUR OVERDUE BALANCE, WE HAVE SOMETHING QUITE UNPLEASANT IN STORE FOR YOU..."

123

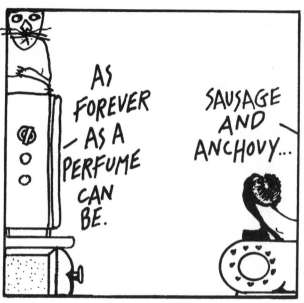

the
End...
Or
is
it?